Trace the word, then write the word yourself.

house

woods

prince

horse

Cinderella

Cinderella wanted to go to the ball. Cinderella's Fairy Godmother waved her wand. It was magic! The mice watched as Cinderella's rags became a beautiful dress.

Trace the word, then write the word yourself.

wand

magic

mice

dress

✵ Sleeping Beauty

Briar Rose was really a princess. She lived with the three good fairies. Briar Rose met Prince Phillip beside the stream. They fell in love.

Trace the word, then write the word yourself.

princess

fairies

stream

love

Ariel

Ariel was a little mermaid. Her friend Flounder was a fish. Her friend Sebastian was a crab. Ariel wanted to live with the humans. She traded her voice to the sea witch for legs, so she would have a chance to live with Prince Eric.

Trace the word, then write the word yourself.

fish

crab

humans

legs

Belle

To save her father, Belle went to live with the Beast in his castle. The Beast and Belle played in the snow. Because Belle loved the Beast, he turned into a handsome prince.